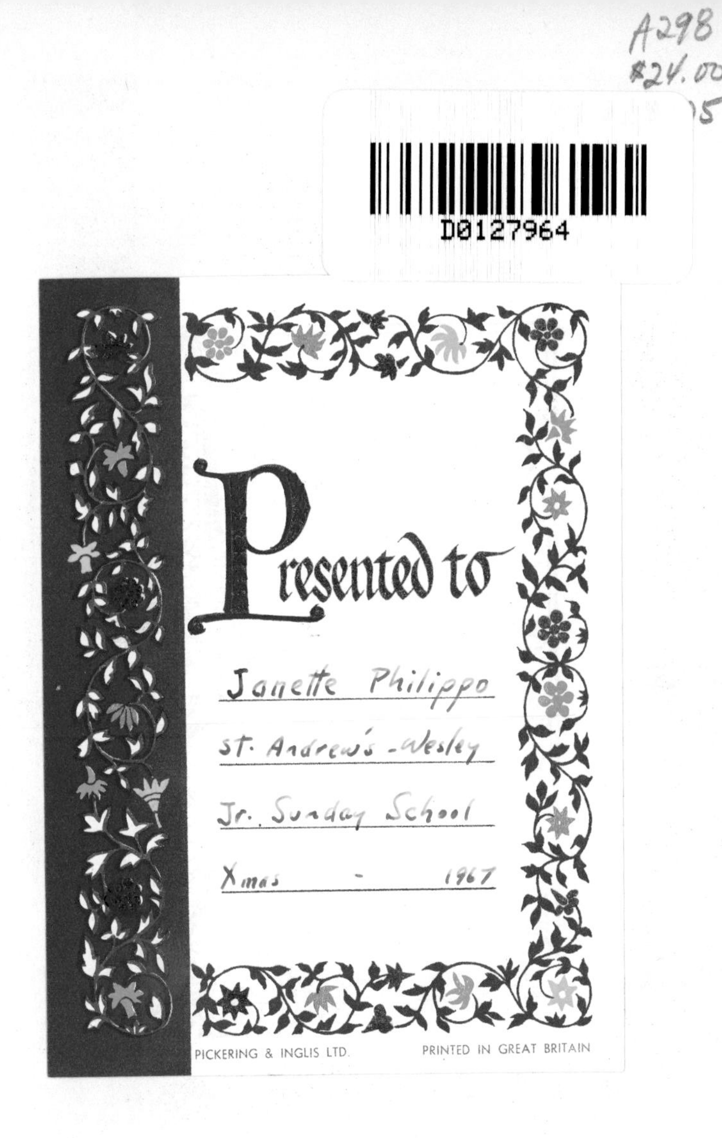
A298
$24.00
D0127964
Presented to
Janette Philippo
St. Andrew's - Wesley
Jr. Sunday School
Xmas - 1967
PICKERING & INGLIS LTD.
PRINTED IN GREAT BRITAIN

By the same Author

THE BOY WITH THE LOAVES AND FISHES
THE LITTLE GIRL AT CAPERNAUM
THE BOY WHO CAME BACK

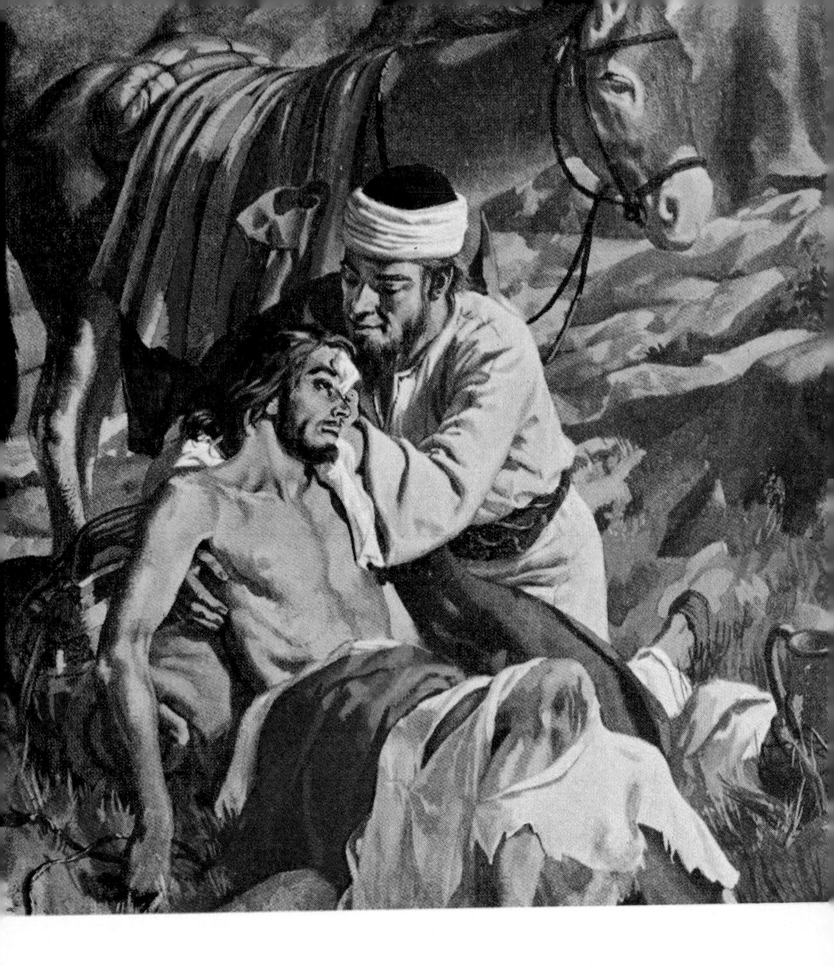

The kind Samaritan bound up the wounds.

The Man Who Stopped to Help

Enid Blyton

Illustrated by
ELSIE WALKER

LUTTERWORTH PRESS
LONDON

First published 1965

*Printed in Great Britain by Richard Clay (The Chaucer Press), Ltd.,
Bungay, Suffolk*

CONTENTS

GOING TO JERUSALEM

This is a tale that Jesus told, and is one of the stories that we should all know. Jesus told it in answer to a question put to him by a clever lawyer. It was a question that could have led to a lot of argument. But Jesus answered it very simply by telling a story. It was a method he often used, and one that all the people loved, and especially the disciples of Jesus. It was by listening that they learned from their Master, just as in any village the people gathered round the wise man of the village, to listen to the stories from their history.

Jesus was with his disciples, on his way

"You should not go to Jerusalem,

to the big city of Jerusalem, where the Temple of God stood.

"You should not go to Jerusalem, Master," said his disciples. "You have enemies there, people who do not want to hear the word of God. You will be in danger."

"My Heavenly Father will protect me," said Jesus. "Let us go."

Master," said his disciples.

So on they went to Jerusalem. Jesus knew that he would not be safe there, for he had enemies in Jerusalem, powerful men who could take him and put him into prison if they wished. These men hated him because he was good and noble, and because the people flocked to hear him preach.

All this had been happening in Galilee,

the country area where Jesus had his home in Nazareth. In Galilee Jesus gathered his little band of disciples and taught them. In Galilee the ordinary people listened to him and knew that here was someone quite different from any preacher they had ever heard. In Galilee Jesus began to realize that he must go with his disciples to Jerusalem, the capital of his country. He could not stay in far-off Galilee. His message must be heard in the big town.

His disciples were afraid of going to the great town of Jerusalem.

"The Pharisees and the priests there will capture Jesus, and throw him into prison, if he dares to preach there," they said fearfully to one another. "What shall we do then, without our beloved master?"

It was a long way to the city of Jerusalem from Galilee, and it was made longer because of the people who crowded round Jesus. Some were ill and begged him to make them well again. Some wanted to hear the stories he so often told, and called out to him, asking him to stop and talk to them. They knew that he helped anyone in trouble or distress. Others were merely sightseers, who hoped to see Jesus perform one of his wonderful miracles.

"If only he would stop and preach to us, he would be sure to see those in the crowd who are ill or maimed," said one man. "Then we should perhaps watch

"He always stops when a child go

one of his miracles; he would touch an ill, unhappy man—and lo, the man would throw away his sticks, and walk after Jesus in joy."

"He must be careful of the rulers of the church," said another man. "They hate him, especially when he preaches to the

him, or someone who is ill."

people, and tells them that the priests and Pharisees do wrong deeds."

"The people all love him," said a woman. "He is so good and kind. He always stops when a child goes to him, or someone who is ill and unhappy."

It was a long way to Jerusalem, and

was made even longer because of the great crowds that tried to get near to Jesus.

"If only I could just touch his cloak!" said a woman. "I have a useless hand—see, I cannot hold anything with it. But if I could get near enough to touch this wonderful man, my hand would be healed."

On and on towards the great city of Jerusalem went the crowds, and the disciples found it difficult to keep them from jostling their master. Even more people joined them, and these asked the crowd around Jesus where everyone was going.

"We go to Jerusalem, to join in the festival there," said one of the disciples.

"Our master is the son of God, and we go with him wherever he goes."

Soon even more travellers joined them, and the disciples were worried. "We shall never be able to find a bed for our master, when we come to a village," said one. "Master, what shall we do if we find all the beds full when we ask for shelter at night?"

"Some of you must hurry on in front," said Jesus. "Ask the people for shelter for the night. Then they will have time to get beds ready."

So the disciples hurried on in front, and came at last to a little village.

"We have no beds," said the people there. "Do you not know that there is a big festival on in Jerusalem, and people come begging us to give them somewhere to sleep on the way? Go on to the next village. Maybe you will find shelter there."

The disciples went to the next village, and asked again for beds for the night. This village was in Samaria, and the Samaritans who lived there disliked the folk who, like the disciples, came from Galilee.

Although they were near neighbours the Jews of Galilee and the people of Samaria were not on speaking terms. When a man from Galilee went up to Jerusalem he took good care to avoid a Samaritan village, and the Samaritans would not give hospitality to someone from Galilee. This unhappy state of

"Go on to the next village."

affairs had come about because the Jews believed that the Temple in Jerusalem was the centre of God's worship, while the Samaritans believed the true home of the Jewish religion was in Samaria.

This old argument between the Jews

and the Samaritans flared up as the disciples walked on through Samaria.

"We are going all the way to Jerusalem," said the disciples. "Can you shelter us to-night?"

"No," said a Samaritan, turning away. "All our beds are full."

The disciples went to another Samaritan. "Sir, we need shelter for the night," they said. "Can you give us somewhere to sleep?"

"No. Go away. We do not want Galileans in our village," said the man rudely.

"We don't give up our beds to people like you," said another man near by.

The disciples were astonished and angry. "Let us go and tell Jesus what bad, selfish people these Samaritans are!"

So they went to Jesus to tell him.

"Dear Lord," they said, "these people, the Samaritans, will not let us sleep for the night in their village!"

"They would even turn away Jesus our Master and Lord!" cried John, one of the disciples.

"They cannot know whom they are turning away!" said James, another disciple.

"Dear Master, punish them!" begged John. "Call down fire from Heaven, so that it may burn up all in this selfish village!"

Jesus looked round at his angry disciples. Did they know him so little that they should expect him to behave in such a way, like a spiteful child?

"Dear Master, punish them!" begged John. "Call down fire from Heaven, so that it may burn up all in this selfish village!"

He looked round at the silent men, and spoke sadly.

"You are wrong," he said. "Do you not know that I have come to save men's lives, not to destroy them? Come, let us leave here and go to the next village."

Jesus turned to walk away, and the disciples followed him, grieved that they had angered him and made him sad. They began to talk among themselves.

"It is no wonder that the Samaritans are hated by everyone," said one disciple in a low voice. "Why should they deny us a night's rest in their villages?"

"They are a mean people," said another.

"A *bad* people," said a third. "No wonder they are hated and despised. I have never heard a good word about them. I feel glad we are not going to sleep the night with them."

Jesus could not help hearing all they said. He was very sad. Not one disciple said a good word for the Samaritans. They had a name for being unhelpful, but Jesus knew there were good people among them, for he had met them himself. How could he make his disciples think differently? Nobody should judge a whole people, and label them all bad!

Jesus knew that His disciples were only saying the things that all the Jews said about the Samaritans. They were repeating the gossip which went on everywhere among the Jews. He did not blame his disciples for what they said, but he was

He did not blame his disciples.

sorry that their hearts were so full of hatred and enmity.

Jesus wondered how he could make his disciples see that they were wrong in their thinking. Perhaps he could tell them a story that would make them change their minds?

WHO IS MY NEIGHBOUR?

Not long afterwards, the little company came to another village.

Jesus and his disciples went among the people, talking and praying.

"Master, where shall we sleep tonight?" asked James, when darkness came. "The people here do not seem to like us. And neither do we like these people."

Now it happened that a very clever man, a lawyer, learned in the law, heard that Jesus the Healer had come to his town.

"The man called Jesus is here," he told his friends. "They say he preaches in a

"I will meet this man Jesus and test him," said the lawyer.

way no man has heard before, and that he can do most wonderful miracles."

"Shall we believe that?" asked another man scornfully. "There is talk, talk, talk of miracles nowadays, but never have I seen one done. No, not one. I will only believe in miracles when I see one, and not before!"

"I will meet this man Jesus and test him," said the lawyer. "We will see what his answers are. He is only a country man, and I do not suppose he will give the right answers."

"Yes, test him," said his friend. "But stand out in front of us all, so that we may hear what you say, and what he answers."

"You may be sure that I shall get the better of our discussion," said the lawyer. "I will make him look foolish before all the people. See what crowds there are to see this man! Why, he might be a king, he has such a welcome!"

"But his name is only Jesus, and he is only from the country," answered his friend.

"I will go to him, and in front of all the people here this man shall try to answer my questions," said the lawyer. "He will not be able to, and the crowd will laugh and jeer. Surely this is the man who goes about calling himself the Son of God? He should be put in prison for saying such a thing!"

The two men elbowed their way through the crowd until they came to Jesus and his disciples. They pushed right up to him, and the lawyer stood in front of him. Everyone could see them and they wondered what was going to happen. The lawyer spoke to Jesus.

"There are some questions I wish to ask you in front of all the people. Are you willing to be tested in this way? Then let us stand together, so that everyone may see and hear!"

Then the lawyer began to ask Jesus questions which he thought would be too difficult to answer. But Jesus answered the questions at once, and then said to the lawyer:

"Now, you know everything about the Laws of God, and what is written there. Tell me what you think is most important in the Law."

"I can answer that a

ce," said the lawyer.

"I can answer that at once," said the lawyer. "The Law says that we must love God with all our heart, with all our soul, and with all our strength, and with all our mind; and we must love our neighbour as much as we love ourselves."

"You are right," said Jesus. "Do these things, and you shall live with God."

"I have still another question," said the man. "Who *is* my neighbour? Can you tell me that?"

"I will tell you," said Jesus. "Listen to this story, and you will know the answer to your question."

And straightaway Jesus began to tell the lawyer, and all those with him, the Tale of the Good Samaritan.

I am sure you will like this story. It is

one of the greatest Jesus told to his followers. Try to imagine that you are in court with all the people who were there listening to Jesus. I have told it in my own words, but if you read the tenth chapter of St. Luke, you will find the story as Jesus told it, in verses 30 to 35.

THE STORY OF THE GOOD SAMARITAN

Once there was a man who was travelling along the mountain road that runs from Jerusalem to Jericho. It was a long and lonely journey, for he was all by himself, and there was no one in sight, no matter where he looked.

He knew that robbers lived among the mountains, waiting for unwary travellers, and he kept a good look-out for them. He stopped every few minutes and looked behind him, for his footsteps echoed on the rocky path, and sounded as if someone were following him.

But he could see nobody, and went on

his way as fast as he could over the rocky, uneven path, through the lonely mountains.

He felt uneasy. Everything was so quiet except for the strong wind that blew into his face. He stopped for a moment and looked all round him.

Nobody to be seen. Nothing moving except that eagle circling in the air over there. "Has somebody disturbed him?" thought the traveller, going on his way again.

He soon left the great eagle behind, and rounded a steep corner of the mountain—and at once he saw mountains upon mountains stretching as far as he could see. He shivered as the wind swept round the corner, and almost sent him over.

What a great, big, lonely world, stretching out below him, and all around him. How far away his home seemed, how great the sky was—and how small he felt with the great mountains around him! He went into a little cave for a rest, and sat there, wishing he was back in his home. The world seemed so vast and big and lonely out here on the mountains.

"I wish I had my dog with me," he thought. "I should not feel this great loneliness then. He would come up and lick my hand, and jump about and bark. It is not good to be all alone in the towering mountains. I will go on my way, and hurry as much as I can. I will whistle a merry tune, and the time will soon pass as I hurry along."

How far away his home seemed.

He jumped up, took his stick and walked quickly out of the friendly little cave. He began to whistle a merry tune as he went along the rocky path as fast as he dared.

"Be careful now," he said to himself. "One foolish step and you will roll right down the mountainside, and maybe end up bruised and battered in a mountain stream. No, no—I must not think such stupid thoughts. I am as sure-footed as a mountain goat! Soon I shall be going downhill to the plain below, and I shall see people working in the far-off fields, and they will wave to me!"

He began singing again, and felt much better. Then he shouted out very loudly, and at once the echoes came back to him, and made him laugh. His laugh echoed too, and he stood listening to it coming back to him from the rocky mountain walls.

"Who is there?" he shouted, in fun. And back came his voice. "Who is there-ere-ere!"

"It's ME!" he shouted, at the top of

his voice. And back came the echo, "ME, ME, ME!"

"It's a good thing there's nobody up here to-day, listening to me," thought the man. But he was wrong—somebody *was* listening to him. A robber who had his cave in the mountains had heard his shouting echoing in the wind, and was even now peering out to see who was the loud shouter.

He gave a low whistle, and from the depths of the cave came three more robbers. This was their hiding-place, the spot where they waited for unwary travellers.

"Quiet," said the first robber, peering out of the cave to see if he could see the shouter. "Ah—there's that shouting again—see, brothers, there is a man on the high rocky walls yonder. He is following that path that brings him outside our cave. Quiet, now."

The shouting and singing grew louder as the traveller leapt from rock to rock on the uneven mountain path, and the robbers crouched back in their cave.

"Let him pass our cave, then we can leap on his back and get him down quickly," said one of the robbers. "Not a sound till you see me jump at him. You follow me with the rope to tie him up."

The merry song sounded very loud now, and so did the traveller's footsteps. The robbers held their breath and stood ready to pounce.

"NOW!" said the leader in a fierce

"Not a sound till you see me jump at him."

whisper as the traveller, still singing, came by the opening of their cave. At once all four leapt from the cave and pounced on the unwary man. He fell to the ground at once, and began to struggle.

"No good struggling," said the leader, hauling the fallen man up from the rocky floor of the cave. "Give us your money. Quickly!"

"You thieves! You robbers!" yelled the poor traveller, trying to struggle free, kicking out with his feet as hard as he could. "Let me go! You'll be sent to prison for this. Let me go!"

But it was no good struggling with such strong, fierce men. They hit him so hard that he fell to the ground and lay there, trying to get his breath. The robbers took

"You thieves! You robbers!"

his leather purse from him and tore it open. Out fell all the man's money, and the robbers began to scrabble on the ground for it, each trying to get the most.

The traveller tried to stand up, but his legs felt so weak that he fell over. One of the robbers laughed.

"Ho! I've a good mind to take you up in my arms, and throw you down the mountain!" he said. "Come now, take off those fine clothes of yours, and give them to me. They're just about my size. And you can give my brother there your fine strong sandals. Come on, take them off, I say."

The poor man began to tremble. "Don't take my clothes," he begged. "It is cold up here on the mountains and I shall freeze to death at night if you leave me without anything to wear."

"Leave him your old cloak," said the chief to one of his men. "It's full of holes for the wind to blow through. You take his fine cloak, and leave yours."

So the poor traveller had his fine warm

cloak ripped off his shoulders, and was thrown a tattered piece of cloth instead. They tied him up with their rope. Then, laughing loudly, the robbers trooped out of the cave, one of them stamping along proudly in the traveller's good strong sandals.

The poor man left behind could hear their loud voices for some time. He was in a bad state, for his feet were bare, he had no warm cloak, his coat had been taken too, and all his money.

He did not know what to do. He had been knocked about by the cruel robbers, and could hardly walk a step. He tried shouting, but his voice had gone. He tried crawling, but the rock was hard on his knees, and they soon began to bleed.

"Perhaps someone will come past the cave," he thought. "I could cry out for help then. The path is not far away, I can see it from here. I will roll over to it, and lie there, hoping for someone to rescue me before the robbers return."

So he rolled painfully over and over from the cave to a patch of grass beside the rocky path. Now no one could fail to see him. He was so tired when he reached the patch of grass that he just lay there, unmoving. Now—if *only* someone would come by. Nobody came, so he tried shouting for help—but all the answer he heard was the echo of his own voice crying, "Help! Help! Oh, help me!"

Then—what a wonderful sound he

heard! It was someone singing softly, and the sound of quiet footsteps.

Pad-pad-pad, went the footsteps, coming nearer and nearer. "Help me, help me!" called the man. "My head is bleeding, I cannot walk. Help!"

The footsteps came nearer. The man lifted his aching head, and was delighted to see who it was.

"A priest! A man of God! He is going to his church at Jerusalem! He will cut my ropes, and give me water, and take me home. Hey, good sir, come nearer here. I have been set on by thieves, and I need help!"

But, to his great surprise, the priest did not come near to him. He stopped when he heard the poor man's voice, but he did not go to him, but passed him as far away as he could. He did not even bother to look at the man's wounds, but went on his way, whistling.

"Ah well," thought the wounded man, "the priest is a busy man. Perhaps he has to get to Jerusalem in time for a ceremony in the Temple. If he touched me and got blood on his hands he would need to go through the purification rites. It would all take time and be very awkward for him."

But he was so thirsty. The wounded man groaned in despair. How could anyone be so cruel?

"Water!" he called. "Give me water to drink!"

But the man of God was gone.

The poor man lying on the ground could not believe that a holy man would pass him by! But wait—he could hear someone else coming. Perhaps he could get help after all. He lifted up his head to see who it was. Ah—it was a Levite, a man who worshipped God, and helped in the church. Surely he would help, surely he would be kind? Ah yes, he was coming over to the cave.

"Help me, please help me!" said the wounded man. "I was attacked and wounded. I am so thirsty, I need water. I want . . ."

The Levite came over to him where he lay. He stared down at him, and saw that the man's clothes and belongings had been stolen, and he saw too that the man was badly wounded and in pain. He stared a little longer, and then, without a single word of comfort, without giving the poor man even a sip of water, he went once more on his way. The poor man was left alone again, sad and disappointed with such unkindness.

He lay there, listening for more footsteps. Surely some kind person would come by soon. Ah—listen—more footsteps! The wounded man lifted his head to see who it was. He knew those footsteps; they were more than the footsteps of one man. "Clop, clop." His heart leaped with hope.

"It's a man—on a little donkey," he thought. "But oh, he comes from Samaria, he is a Samaritan." He saw by

He stared a little longer.

the man's dress, and the trim of his beard, that he was not from Jerusalem or Jericho. He had the look of a foreigner about him. Yes, he was a Samaritan. The wounded man sank back in despair. This man, he thought, will never help me, even if he should catch sight of me.

"I've been told that they are bad people, those Samaritans of Samaria. Why, the priests and the Levites will not even lie down to rest in the house of a Samaritan. He'll never help me! I am lost!"

Then what a surprise the man had! The Samaritan had seen him, and knew that he was wounded and in need of help —he was coming to him—he had laid a cool hand on the man's hot, bleeding head. He was talking to him in a kind voice.

"You poor fellow!" he said, kneeling down by the man. "I see you have been robbed and badly beaten. Lie still for a while and I will do what I can to make you better."

The man felt his wounds being gently rubbed with oil and wine. Then the kind Samaritan bound up the wounds with bits of cloth.

"Now, my poor fellow, try to get up," he said. "Gently now—I'm helping you. Lean on my strong arms. Here's my little donkey patiently waiting for us. I'll lift you up on his back. Then we will go to an inn, and you shall have some food and drink."

It was a long way down the track to the nearest inn. The wounded man knew it well. He had often stopped there on his way to Jericho, so he was pleased when his new friend turned the donkey's head that way. The innkeeper would be kind; but, alas, all his money had been stolen. Who would pay the bill? This question worried him as he struggled on to the donkey's back.

So off they went, the good Samaritan leading the little donkey, and helping to hold the man on his back, so that he would not fall off.

At last they came to the inn, and the Samaritan called for the innkeeper.

"Have you a room for this poor man?" he said. "He has been attacked and

He struggled on to the donkey's back.

robbed, and he needs care and sleep. I will look after him to-night, and to-morrow I shall leave him here in your care until he is quite better."

The inn was only a rough shelter. Although it was roomy and had a man

in charge of it, travellers were expected to look after themselves. They brought their own food and drink, and while straw was provided by the inn every traveller had to make his own bed. So

As he lay on the straw he noticed that his Samaritan friend was looking after someone else.

when the wounded man heard the Samaritan say that he would look after him during the night he was doubly thankful.

Clean straw was put down, and he was

laid on it with great care. The warmth of the shelter made up for the loss of his new cloak, and the bruises and cuts on his body were soon less painful.

As he lay on the straw he noticed that his Samaritan friend was also busy looking after someone else. At the end of the long shelter, munching away very happily, was the donkey. He too was given fresh straw for his bed, and the wounded man went to sleep knowing that he now had two friends under that roof, and that both of them came from Samaria a land that he had been taught to hate. The wounded man never forgot that night in the inn.

All that night the good Samaritan looked after the poor hurt man. When morning came he had to leave, but before he went he gave the innkeeper some money for him.

"Take great care of that man for me," he said. "Spend what money you have to. I will pay you back when next I come by."

Then he said good-bye to the grateful man and went on his way.

Jesus had told this story in such a way that not one person said a word until he had finished. Those who had thought the Samaritans bad people felt ashamed. No one could have been better or kinder than the good Samaritan in the story.

"I have told you this story so that you may know what it is to have a good friend," said Jesus. "Now I will ask you all a question, which you must answer in your own hearts. Which of the three, the priest, the Levite, and Samaritan, was a good friend to the man who fell among thieves?"

Can you answer that? Of course you can—and I feel certain that you too will always try to be a good friend, a "good Samaritan".